South & West Suite

Four movements for organ by
Barry Ferguson

South & West Suite

Four movements for organ by
Barry Ferguson

Kevin Mayhew

We hope you enjoy the music in *The South and West Suite.*
Further copies of are available from
your local music shop or Christian bookshop.

In case of difficulty, please contact the publisher direct by writing to:

The Sales Department
KEVIN MAYHEW LTD
Rattlesden
Bury St Edmunds
Suffolk IP30 0SZ

Phone 0449 737978
Fax 0449 737834

Please ask for our complete catalogue of outstanding Church Music.

Front Cover: *Exeter from Exwick* by William Traies (1789-1872).
Royal Albert Memorial Museum, Exeter/Bridgeman Art Library, London.
Reproduced by kind permission.

Cover designed by Juliette Clarke and Graham Johnstone.
Picture Research: Jane Rayson.
Music Editor: Anthea Smith.

First published in Great Britain in 1993 by Kevin Mayhew Ltd

© Copyright 1993 Kevin Mayhew Ltd

ISBN 0 86209 341 4

Printed and bound in Great Britain.

Contents

BARRY FERGUSON was born in 1942 and first sat at an organ as a five year-old in Peters Marland Church in North Devon, where his mother was organist. He went on to study with Reginald Moore as Head Chorister at Exeter Cathedral, with Sir David Willcocks at Peterhouse, Cambridge, and with Herbert Howells for Composition. He was Assistant Organist at Peterborough Cathedral in the vintage years of Dr Stanley Vann, and Organist of Wimborne Minster in Dorset. He has been Organist and Master of the Choristers at Rochester Cathedral since 1977, and conducts the Rochester Choral Society.

Barry Ferguson enjoys variety in his compositions. In addition to church music, he has written song cycles and film music, and composed a canon in praise of Italian ice cream. His setting of *The Lord looseth men out of prison*, written to celebrate the release of Terry Waite, was performed before the Archbishop of Canterbury in his private chapel. He also writes poetry.

Foreword

". . .And citizens dream of the south and west,
And so do I. . ."

The title *The South and West*, a quotation from the first verse of Thomas Hardy's poem *Weathers*, brings together many of the strands of thought behind this organ work, commissioned by Robert Crowley with funds made available by the Ralph Vaughan Williams Trust.

The South: Joy Finzi, the composer Gerald Finzi's widow, lived in Berkshire, and died in June 1991. She had encouraged me as a composer for more than 25 years and I wanted to write a joyful piece in her memory. I also wanted to write pieces for two special colleagues, Roger Sayer, my assistant at Rochester Cathedral, and David Price, the Organ Scholar.

The West: Sandi, my wife, likes Pavanes. A visit to the elegant Saltram House at Plymouth, and also studying the Fitzwilliam Virginal Book, were starting points for *Pavana Chromatica*. Sandi is half Scottish, and this is hinted at.

The North Devon landscape, especially the Bideford and Torrington area, has been an inspiration since childhood. In particular, the *Pastorale* was inspired by *A View of Bideford from Upcott Hill* by an unknown artist (c.1845) in the permanent collection of the Burton Art Gallery, Bideford. I composed this Suite nearby at our cottage 'West Loatmead', bought in 1972, the year in which Rachel was born. Here the air is clean, the light is radiant, and sunsets are a time of great peace and wonderful changing colours.

The first performance was given by myself at the Parish Church of St. Michael and All Angels, Great Torrington, North Devon, on 29th April 1992.

BARRY FERGUSON

BIDEFORD PASTORALE

Barry Ferguson

Mrs Sandi Ferguson's Paven

PAVANA CHROMATICA

Barry Ferguson

This piece, written for manuals only, could be performed on the harpsichord or piano.

14

16

TOCCATA FOR JOY

Barry Ferguson

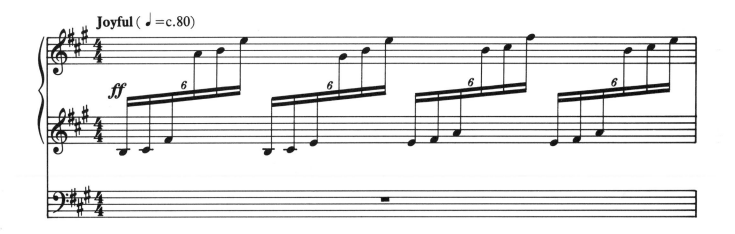

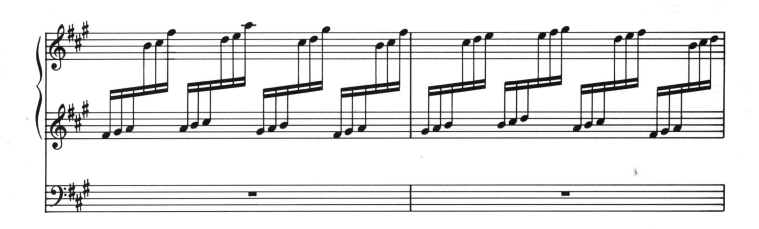

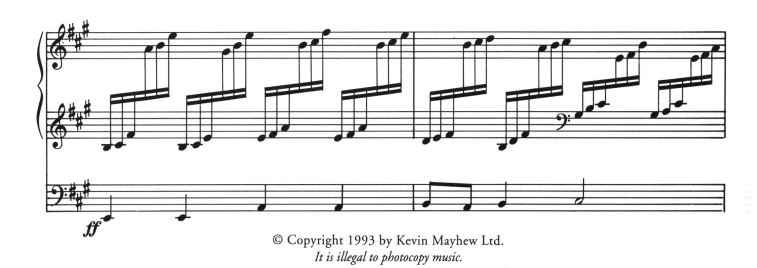

25

For R.M.F.

SUNSET AT WEST LOATMEAD

Barry Ferguson